FUTURAMA
THE TIME BENDER TRILOGY

HARPER

NEW YORK . LONDON . TORONTO . SYDNEY

FUTURAMA: THE TIME BENDER TRILOGY

HarperCollinsPublishers
77-85 Fulham Palace Road,
Hammersmith, London W6 8JB
www.harpercollins.co.uk

This edition first published 2006

ISBN-10: 0-00-723454-6
ISBN-13 978-0-00-723454-7
1 3 5 7 9 8 6 4 2

Publisher: MATT GROENING

Creative Director: BILL MORRISON

Managing Editor: TERRY DELEGEANE

Director of Operations: ROBERT ZAUGH

Art Director: NATHAN KANE

Art Director Special Projects: SERBAN CRISTESCU

Production Manager: CHRISTOPHER UNGAR

Legal Guardian: SUSAN A. GRODE

Trade Paperback Concepts and Design: SERBAN CRISTESCU

PRINTED IN CANADA

THE TIME BENDER TRILOGY
(in four parts)

CHAPTER 1 — 5

Story by IAN BOOTHBY
Pencils by JAMES LLOYD
Inks by STEVE STEERE JR.
Colors by JOEY MASON
Letters by KAREN BATES

CHAPTER 2 — 34

Story by IAN BOOTHBY
Pencils by JOHN DELANEY
Inks by PHYLLIS NOVIN
Colors by JOEY MASON
Letters by KAREN BATES

CHAPTER 3 — 62

Story by IAN BOOTHBY
Pencils by JOHN DELANEY
Inks by PHYLLIS NOVIN
Colors by JOEY MASON
Letters by KAREN BATES

CHAPTER 4 — 90

Story by IAN BOOTHBY
Pencils by JOHN DELANEY
Inks by PHYLLIS NOVIN
Colors by JOEY MASON
Letters by KAREN BATES

COVER GALLERY — 117

BAD NEWS, EVERYONE! I HAD ZOIDBERG TAKE CUBERT'S *INTELLECTUAL TEMPERATURE* WITH THIS *I.Q. THERMOMETER.*

WHY COULDN'T IT HAVE BEEN AN *ORAL* THERMOMETER?

IT *WAS.*

I JUST HAVE VERY BAD AIM. *SORRY!*

CUBERT'S I.Q. HAS DROPPED 5 POINTS. HE'S GONE FROM "A+"S TO "A"S. HE'S JUST A GENIUS, NOT A *SUPER GENIUS.*

AW, I'M SORRY YOU'RE STUPID, KID. HERE'S A SHINY OBJECT FOR YOU TO LOOK AT!

OOOOH.

HEY, *MY WATCH!*

OH PLEASE, NEXT TO THE THREE OF YOU I'M THE CO-CLONE OF *EINSTEIN* AND *BRANIAC 5!*

OH, SO YOU THINK I'M NOT SMART, ARE I?

WELL...

8

THE PLANET AQUARIUS XII

SO THE ENTIRE SCHOOL IS UNDER-WATER?

YES, THE CLASSROOMS, THE LABS, THE GYM, EVERYTHING IS UNDERWATER EXCEPT FOR THE SWIMMING POOL. THAT'S ABOVE GROUND. IT WAS MUCH CHEAPER.

SO WHAT BRINGS YOU HERE?

THE PROFESSOR WANTS TO SEE CUBERT'S GRADES GO UP.

OH, WE DON'T HAVE GRADES HERE.

Y-Y-YOU D-D-DON'T?

NO, WE REWARD GOOD WORK WITH OXYGEN!

KEEPS THE CHILDREN MOTIVATED!

BZZZAP!

YES, WELL YOU SHOULD HAVE THOUGHT ABOUT BREATHING BEFORE YOU HANDED IN THAT BOOK REPORT.

MMMPH!

THE COUNT OF MONTE CRISTO WAS NOT A VAMPIRE!

LATER...

HEY, FRY, PICK A NUMBER BETWEEN ONE AND INFINITY.

UM... 1,274,549?

TELEPAX

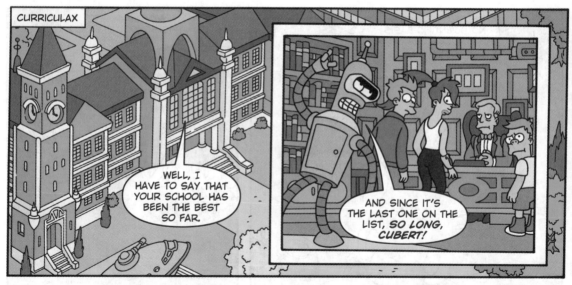

CURRICULAX

WELL, I HAVE TO SAY THAT YOUR SCHOOL HAS BEEN THE BEST SO FAR.

AND SINCE IT'S THE LAST ONE ON THE LIST, *SO LONG, CUBERT!*

WE'D BE PLEASED TO ADD YOUNG CUBERT TO OUR STUDENT BODY.

WE HAVE OVER *ONE MILLION* STUDENTS AT THE PRESENT TIME AND...

BBRRIIIIIINNNNGG!!!

FIRE DRILL!

ALL RIGHT, STUDENTS, EVERYONE LINE UP OUT-SIDE, SINGLE *FILE!*

WHY AREN'T YOU AT THE BACK OF THE LINE, STUDENT?

BECAUSE I'M AT THE *FRONT* OF THE LINE.

MAN, YOU EITHER NEED LESS STUDENTS OR A BIGGER PLANET.

WE'RE PROUD OF OUR POLICY OF ACCEPTING *EVERYONE* WHO APPLIES NO MATTER GRADE POINT AVERAGE, AGE, OR MOLECULAR DENSITY.

15

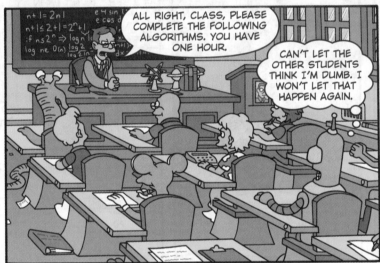

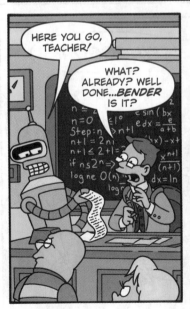

OKAY, THIS IS GONNA BE FINE. NOT *ALL* GYM TEACHERS ARE SOCIOPATHS.

HEY, LISTEN, I'M NEW. HOW CAN I MAKE A GOOD IMPRESSION ON THE TEACHER?

OH, YOU SHOULD START BY DOING SOME EXERCISES ON YOUR OWN.

is it in you

THEN SEEK MEDICAL HELP IMMEDIATELY

REALLY?

OH, YEAH, MR. DELTOID REALLY APPRECIATES IT WHEN STUDENTS SHOW INITIATIVE AND INDEPENDENT THOUGHT.

WHAT ARE YOU DOING? *UNAUTHORIZED EXERCISE?!!!*

HUH?

SNICKER!

YAAAAH!

WHAT'S THE MATTER, BOY? YOU'VE NEVER SEEN A MAN WHOSE MUSCULATURE WAS SO PERFECT THAT HE HAD HIS SKIN REMOVED TO SHARE IT WITH THE WORLD?

NO, THIS IS NEW...

...DISTURBINGLY NEW.

LATER...

OH, MAN, LEELA, THIS IS SO COOL!

SHOULDN'T WE BE GETTING BACK? WE'LL BE LATE FOR CLASS.

NOT IF YOU SLINGSHOT AROUND THE SUN AND GO BACK IN TIME AN HOUR OR SO.

I DON'T KNOW. I HEAR THAT'S REALLY BAD FOR THE SUN!

GEEZ, LEELA, AND WE THOUGHT YOU WERE SO COOL.

I'M COOL! I'M COOL! SEE?

DANGER! NO SLINGSHOTING

BENDER, I NEED YOUR *HELP!*

I WAS WITH SOME GIRLS, AND WE SLINGSHOTTED AROUND THE SUN, AND I THINK WE TRIGGERED A SUPERNOVA.

DON'T WORRY, LEELA. I KNOW *JUST* WHAT TO DO!

DEAN! DEAN! LEELA BROKE THE SUN!

YOU LITTLE FINK! I'M GOING TO GET YOU AFTER CLASS BY THE BIKE RACKS!

WHAT'S WRONG, MAGGOT? HUFF IT GETTING TO HOT FOR YOU? HUFF POOR BABY CAN'T TAKE THE HEAT? WELL, MAYBE A FEW MORE *LAPS* HUFF WILL COOL YOU DOWN. HUFF

IT MUST BE EVEN WORSE FOR YOU WITHOUT *SWEAT GLANDS.*

THUD!

FRY! PUT DOWN THAT HUGE PIECE OF BEEF JERKY AND COME WITH ME!

SURE. WHAT UP?

THE SUN'S BLOWING UP, AND LEELA'S IN DETENTION. WE NEED TO TAKE THE SHIP AND GET OUT OF HERE.

NO! NOT WITHOUT LEELA AND TO A LESSER EXTENT CUBERT AND THE OTHER STUDENTS AND TEACHERS.

SIGH ...FINE. WE'LL SAVE EVERY-BODY.

MAYBE I'LL GET EXTRA CREDIT FOR THIS. THEN MY GPA WILL BE SO HIGH MY CLASS-MATES WILL *HAVE* TO RESPECT ME.

LATER, IN DETENTION HALL...

YOU'RE NOT LISTENING...

NO, *YOU'RE* NOT LISTENING. THE SCHOOL YEAR DOESN'T END UNTIL THE SUMMER IN *FOUR MONTHS.*

THE SUN IS GOING TO FRY US ALL. YOU DON'T GET MORE *SUMMER* THAN THAT.

I'M SORRY, RULES ARE RULES. NO STUDENT CAN LEAVE THE SCHOOL GROUNDS UNTIL AFTER THE SEMESTER.

I HAVE AN IDEA!

GAH! CUBERT?

WE...

FORGOT ABOUT ME. YES, I KNOW! I HAVE A PLAN THAT COULD SAVE US ALL. BUT, DEAN, YOU HAVE TO LET US LEAVE THE SCHOOL.

ZOIDBERG? AMY? WHERE *IS* EVERYBODY?!

THAT'S WEIRD. WHY WOULD THEY LEAVE IN SUCH A HURRY THEY LEFT THEIR WORK LOCKERS OPEN?

YEAH, *ANY-ONE* COULD STEAL THEIR STUFF!

IT'S NOT JUST THE OFFICE! COME OUTSIDE!

THIS IS CREEPY. TWILIGHT ZONE CREEPY.

THE GOOD VERSION, NOT THE MOVIE OR THE TWO CRAPPY TV REMAKES.

ACCORDING TO A PERIMETER SCAN ON MY WRIST THINGAMABOB, WE'RE THE ONLY SENTIENT BEINGS LEFT...

IN THE CITY?

ON *EARTH*.

THE TIME BENDER TRILOGY CHAPTER 2

OKAY, FINE. THEN *YOU* COME UP WITH ANOTHER WAY FOR US TO REPOPULATE THE PLANET.

HOW ABOUT THE CLONING TANK?

I'VE BEEN USING IT FOR PICKLING. YOU JUST CAN'T GET GOOD GHERKINS AROUND HERE.

GOOD NEWS, EVERYONE!

HEY! GET YOUR *OWN* CATCH-PHRASE!

BUT I REALLY *DO* HAVE GOOD NEWS. I FOUND THREE BROKEN PIECES OF WHAT SEEM TO BE A NEW INVENTION.

THEY APPEAR TO BE RECENTLY USED, AND I'M GETTING REALLY STRONG CHRONITON READINGS FROM THEM.

THE KIND USED IN TIME MACHINES?

THEORETICALLY, BUT THE ODDS ARE...

FWOOSH!

AAAAAH!

cAAAAAW!

SO IT *IS* A TIME MACHINE, AND IT WAS ACTIVATED WHEN WE PUT THE PIECES TOGETHER.

BUT IT'S *MISSING* A PART. I CAN'T TURN IT OFF.

SO WE HAVE A *TIME HOLE.* WE HAVE *BIGGER* PROBLEMS! WE NEED TO FIND *96* PEOPLE FAST. *97* IF CUBERT'S BEEN EATEN.

FRY! *BEHIND YOU!*

HUH?

BACK YOU GO!

BENDER! *QUIT* IT!

OH, SORRY, YOU LOOKED LIKE A NEANDERTHAL.

HEY! IS ANYONE THERE?

44

45

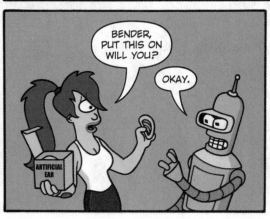

57

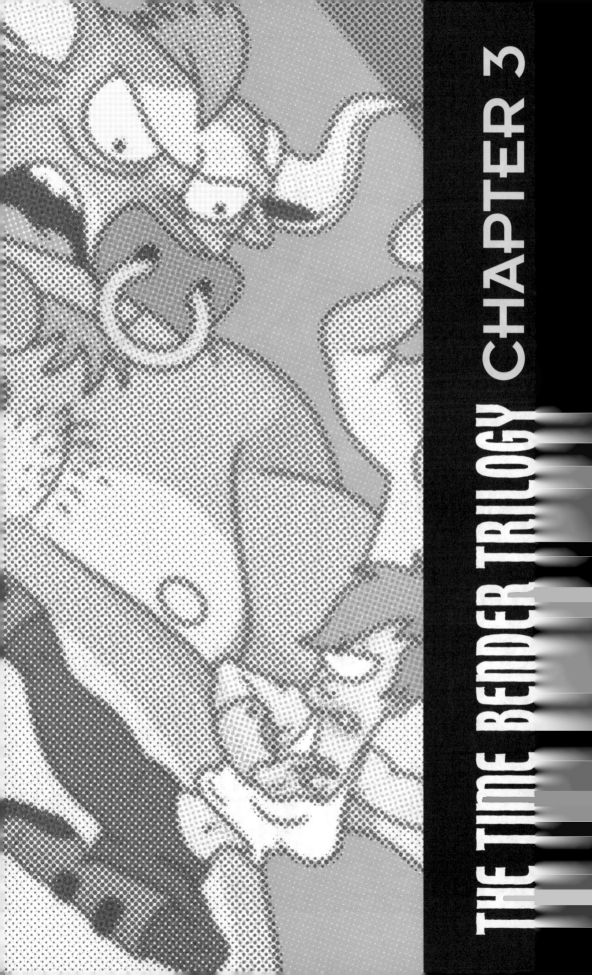

THE TIME BENDER TRILOGY CHAPTER 3

"THE PROFESSOR WAS ABLE TO BREAK OFF A PIECE OF THE TIME MACHINE AND TAKE IT INTO THE PAST WITH HIM. FRY, LEELA, AND BENDER WERE GIVEN THE SIMPLE TASK OF BRINGING THE REST OF THE MACHINE BACK AND SAVING THE WORLD."

"BUT DUE TO A SEVERE CASE OF STUPID, FRY CAUSED ALL OF THEM TO BE SUCKED INTO A TIME VORTEX, BREAKING THE REST OF THE TIME MACHINE INTO THREE PIECES IN THE PROCESS."

SORRY FOR DOOMING THE WORLD, GUYS.

SIGH.

I'M SORRY, IS SOMEONE TALKING?

LEAVING ME, CUBERT FARNSWORTH, THE LAST BOY ON EARTH.

I'M TRYING TO LOCATE PLANET EXPRESS'S THREE STOOGES WITH THE HELP OF MY ROBOT MONKEY, WHO I'VE NAMED "ASTERISK."

ERR-AH-AH-EEP!

MAKE YOUR OWN
ROBOT
MONKEY KIT

AGES 6 AND UP

THAT'S RIGHT, ASTERISK, IF WE WAIT TOO LONG, THE CHANGES TO THE TIME STREAM WILL BECOME *PERMANENT* AND THE PRESENT WILL *CEASE TO EXIST!*

OKAY, LET'S GET TO WORK! THOSE IDIOTS AREN'T GOING TO FIND THEMSELVES.

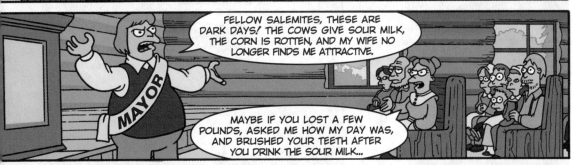

MEANWHEN AGAIN...

WAKE UP, MAGGOT!

I AM AWAKE, SIR!

NOT YOU, PRIVATE LARVOWSKI!

GROAN!

WHY ARE YOU OUT OF UNIFORM, PRIVATE?

MOAN WHAT YEAR IS IT?

1915! AND IF YOU THINK YOU CAN GET OUT OF DUTY BY PLAYING CRAZY, THEN YOU ARE CRAZY!

BUT NOT CRAZY ENOUGH TO GET OUT OF DUTY!

THIS IS WORLD WAR 1?

WORLDS WAR 1!

ARMY OUTFIT NOW WITH LASER RIFLE

COUGH! COUGH!

PFFFFT!

COOL!

THIS IS JUST A *COINCIDENCE.* FREAK LIGHTING STORMS HAPPEN AROUND MOUNTAINS ALL THE TIME*!*

THERE ARE *NO* GODS!

WILL YOU *SHUT UP!*

HUH?

WSSSSSSH!

YOU HAVE DISPLEASED THE GODS WITH YOUR *BLASPHEMY!*

WHAT ARE YOU? THE GOD OF FLOWER DELIVERY MASCOTS?

I AM *HERMES,* MESSENGER OF THE GODS!

REALLY? I WORK WITH SOMEONE WITH THE SAME NAME. HE'S KIND OF A TIGHT ASS.

LISTEN, I DON'T REALLY BUY INTO THIS "GODS" BUSINESS. BUT IF YOU REALLY ARE ON THE LEVEL, CAN YOU GUYS SEND ME INTO THE PAST?

PERHAPS!

YOINK!

WSSSSSSSSSSSSSSSSSSSSH!

BACK IN THE TRENCHES...

HOW WAS THE PACIFIC?

COUGH! HACK!

THIS STRAIGHT. WE'RE FIGHTING OMICRON PERSEI 8?

JUST 8? I WISH! IT'S THE WHOLE EMPIRE, 1 THROUGH 27.

THEY FEEL EARTH HAS EVOLVED TOO QUICKLY AND IS A DANGER TO THE UNIVERSE.

IT MUST BE BECAUSE OF THE TIME MACHINE. IT CHANGED EVERYTHING.

SAY WHAT?

NOTHING. ARE YOU FROM EARTH?

OH, HEAVENS NO. I'M A MAGGOTIAN. JUST ONE OF SEVERAL RACES THAT FEEL THIS INVASION IS UNJUST AND HAVE JOINED IN YOUR FIGHT.

PLUS, IF YOU LOSE, THERE SHOULD BE A LOT OF CORPSES.

SO FOR US IT'S REALLY A WIN-WIN SITUATION!

ENOUGH CHIN-WAGGIN'! MAN YOUR GUNS!

WE'RE UNDER ATTACK!

REALLY? WHERE?

LOOK CLOSER. SHE'S THE ONE LIVING IN THE SPLIT LEVEL LABYRINTH.

JUST BEND OVER, AND YOU'LL SEE IT.

YAAAAAAAAAAAAAH!

BOOT!

MEANWHILE...

HEY, BUDDY. MISSING YOUR GIRL?

SHE'S NOT REALLY MY GIRL. SHE'S...

...YEAH, I GUESS I AM.

MY SUSIE, SHE'S THE BEST. BEFORE I LEFT, SHE GAVE ME THIS *GOOD LUCK CHARM* AND MADE ME PROMISE NEVER TO TAKE IT OFF.

CAN I SEE IT?

SURE! WHY NOT?

MEANWHILE ON MOUNT OLYMPUS...

HA! I MADE IT!

GOD ONLY PARKING

WELL DONE, MORTAL! ZEUS WILL SEE YOU NOW!

SO, YOU ARE THE MORTAL WHO DID SLAY THE MINOTAUR AND FREED MY KITTENS?

NOW YOU ARE HERE TO ASK ME FOR A *BOON*?

YES, AND I'D LIKE TO THANK YOU FOR THE CHANCE TO TALK TO YOU IN A CALM AND REASONABLE MANNER. I'M FROM THE FUTURE, AND EVEN THOUGH I THINK YOU'RE A BUNCH OF NONSENSE, I...

KA*BOOM!*

MOAN! I'M GETTING *REAL* TIRED OF ASKING THIS, BUT...

...WHERE AM I...?

HADES, LAND OF THE DEAD. NOW GET ON THE FERRY WITH THE OTHER CORPSES!

THE TIME BENDER TRILOGY CHAPTER 4

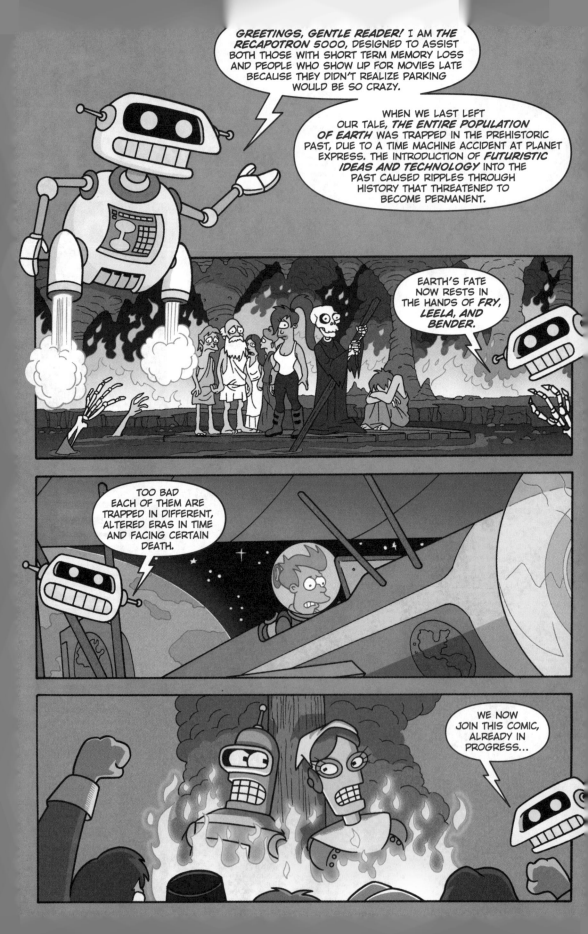

"SO THE NEXT DAY, I WAS IN MY UNDERWEAR PLAYING WITH A PADDLEBALL WHEN..."

WE'VE RUN EVERY TEST POSSIBLE ON THE EARTHLING, YOUR GREATNESS.

AND THE RESULTS?

WHAPPITA WHAPPITA

GAACK!

HE'S AN *IDIOT*.

IS STUPIDITY CONTAGIOUS?

SMACK!

VERY. HAVE YOU HAD ANY SYMPTOMS, MY LORD?

I.... HAVE BEEN WATCHING MORE *REALITY SHOWS* LATELY.

GASP!

GET AWAY FROM ME! *DON'T TOUCH ME!*

SO I'M FREE TO GO?

YES! YOU AND EVERYONE YOU HAD CONTACT WITH! JUST GET OUT BEFORE YOU DUMB THE PLACE DOWN ANY MORE!

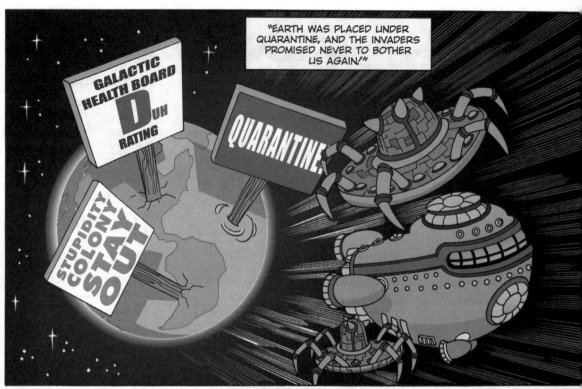

105

OH MY GODS!

THEY'RE *DEAD!*

DEAD *DRUNK*, YOU MEAN. THAT'S WHAT THESE FESTIVALS ARE ALL ABOUT. THEY RECHARGE ON BOOZE AND DRINK UNTIL THEY PASS OUT. THEY WON'T BE REBOOTING FOR HOURS!

THAT GIVES ME SOME TIME. NOW, IF I CAN ONLY REMEMBER MY FOURTH GRADE ROBOTICS REWIRING CLASS.

"I GAVE IT MY BEST SHOT AND SURE ENOUGH, TWO HOURS LATER..."

OH, MY HEAD! I *SWEAR* TO *ME*, I'LL NEVER DRINK AGAIN!

HEY, ZEUS, YOU KNOW SOMETHING? YOU'RE GREAT!

MAYBE IT'S THE AMBROSIA TALKING, BUT YOU'RE GREAT, TOO. YOU TOO, ATHENA!

YOU'RE ALL GREAT!

WHAT DID YOU DO?

REPROGRAMMED THEM TO BE SELF-WORSHIPING. THEY'LL BE TOO BUSY KISSING EACH OTHER'S BUTTS TO BOTHER GREECE.

107

SO WHAT ABOUT THE LAST 400 YEARS? ARE YOU STILL WITH SAMANTHA?

NAW, WE GREW IN DIFFERENT DIRECTIONS... DIDN'T WANT TO RUIN OUR FRIENDSHIP...IT WAS A MUTUAL...

SHE DUMPED YOU?

RIGHT AFTER WE GOT OFF THE STAKE.

I BUMMED AROUND EUROPE... TOOK A POTTERY CLASS...

OH, AND...

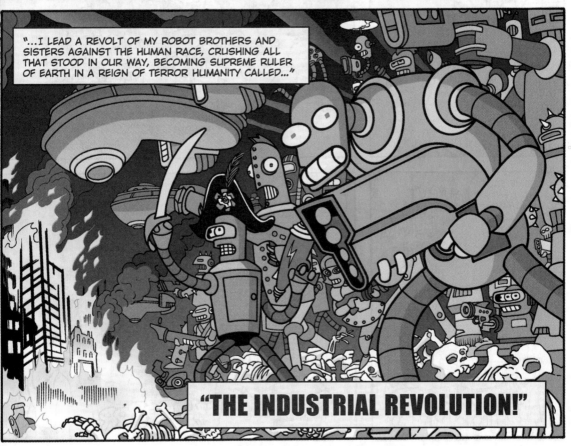

"...I LEAD A REVOLT OF MY ROBOT BROTHERS AND SISTERS AGAINST THE HUMAN RACE, CRUSHING ALL THAT STOOD IN OUR WAY, BECOMING SUPREME RULER OF EARTH IN A REIGN OF TERROR HUMANITY CALLED..."

"THE INDUSTRIAL REVOLUTION!"

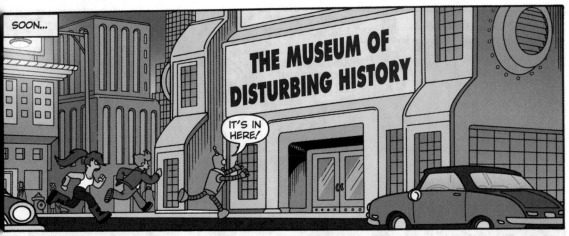

I'M OKAY! HE FORGOT TO CHEW!

OH MY! ONLY *I* KNOW HOW TO MAKE THE MACHINE TAKE US ALL *FORWARDS IN TIME.* BUT THERE'S NO WAY I CAN GET TO IT.

TOSS!

CHOMP!

IT'S *RISKY,* BUT I HOPE YOUR PLAN WORKS, HERMES.

WHAT PLAN IS THAT?

OH HI, PROFESSOR!

SIGH GIVE ME THAT MACHINE!

POT!

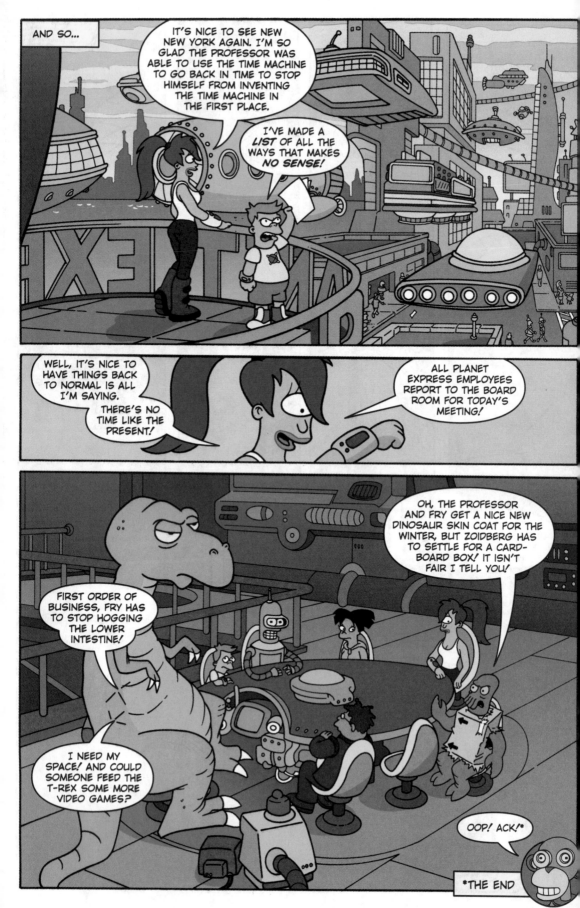